Table of Contents

MW00844081

System Requirements

What do you need?

- Windows 3.1, Windows 95 or later
- 486, Pentium or better (33 MHz or faster recommended)
- Hard disk with 2 MB free (Windows 95) or 5 MB free (Windows 3.1)
- 8 MB memory (RAM)
- Super VGA graphics, 640x480, 256 colors or more
- Double-speed (2X) or faster CD-ROM drive
- Windows-compatible sound card

Optional:

- Windows-compatible printer

Setup Instructions

The installer places a small amount of necessary information on your hard drive to make it easy for children to run *Zoo Zillions*.

Follow these steps to install *Zoo Zillions* on the computer:

For Windows 95 or later:

Insert the CD, then follow these steps.

If AutoPlay is enabled:

1. Installation starts automatically.
2. Follow the on-screen instructions to complete the installation.
3. After installation, reinsert the CD to run *Zoo Zillions*. The Startup Screen appears. Click the **PLAY!** button.

If AutoPlay is not enabled:

1. Choose *Run* from the Start menu and type **d:\setup** (where **d** represents your CD-ROM drive).
2. Follow the on-screen instructions to install the program.
3. After installation, the *Zoo Zillions* icon can be found on the StartlProgramslHarcourt Brace MathematicslMighty Math Zoo Zillions menu. To run *Zoo Zillions*, insert the CD and use the Start menu.

For other versions of Windows:

1. Insert the *Zoo Zillions* CD into your CD-ROM drive.
2. Choose *Run* from the File menu in Program Manager and type **d:\setup** (where **d** represents your CD-ROM drive).
3. Follow the on-screen instructions to install the program.
4. After installation, the *Zoo Zillions* icon can be found in the Harcourt Brace Mathematics program group. To run *Zoo Zillions*, insert the CD and double-click the icon.

Running Mighty Math Zoo Zillions from KidDesk

KidDesk is a personalized, colorful program launcher for children. If you choose to run *Zoo Zillions* from *KidDesk*, use *Add Application* from the *KidDesk* Adult Section to place *Zoo Zillions* ("mathzoo.exe") on your children's desktops. If you have *KidDesk Family Edition* for Windows 95, *Zoo Zillions* may automatically be added for you. Please see *KidDesk* Aware (page 26) for additional information.

System Requirements

What do you need?

- System 7.0.1 or higher
- 68040, 68030 (25 MHz or faster recommended), or PowerPC
- 4 MB memory (RAM), 1900K unused, 5 MB for System 7.5 or later, 8 MB highly recommended
- 13" or larger monitor, 256 or more colors
- Double-speed (2X) or faster CD-ROM drive

Optional:

- Printer

Setup Instructions

1. Insert the CD-ROM.
2. Double-click the *Zoo Zillions* icon.

Running Mighty Math Zoo Zillions from KidDesk

KidDesk is a personalized, colorful program launcher for children. If you choose to run *Zoo Zillions* from *KidDesk*, use *Add Application* from the *KidDesk* Adult Section to place *Zoo Zillions* on your children's desktops. Please see *KidDesk Aware* (page 26) for additional information.

Communication

Mathematics is a language, a language that involves speaking, listening, reading, writing, representing, and thinking. It is through communication that children make sense of the world. Communicating about mathematics helps children make connections between their oral and written language and the symbolism in mathematics. It also helps children clarify and verify their thinking and deepen their understanding of important concepts and ideas.

Speaking, listening, reading, writing, and representing are communication skills that help children develop a foundational conceptual understanding of mathematics. In strong mathematics programs, each of the following important communication skills and strategies is developed.

Speaking and Listening

- Children discuss important math concepts, verbalize their own thinking, and listen to others.
- In cooperative learning activities, children focus on speaking and listening.
- In school-home connections, children communicate with family members about the mathematics they are learning.

Reading

- In reading math, children apply the same good reading strategies they apply in reading other materials.
- Through the integration of literature, children extend math concepts with their use of trade books and Big Books.
- In problem-solving lessons, children focus on developing reading and comprehension strategies essential to good problem solvers.

Writing

- Children formulate their own problems and questions.
- They explain their answers in writing and give written explanations of procedures.
- They keep a Math Journal to help them understand math vocabulary and relate mathematics to their daily lives.

Representing

- Children learn to express, or represent, ideas in new and different formats.
- Children use representations such as diagrams, drawings, and charts to help them understand mathematical ideas.

What's Inside Mighty Math Zoo Zillions

Entering the Zoo

At the Zoo Entrance, you can choose from five fun learning activities. To enter an activity, click one of the five areas shown below. From any activity, click 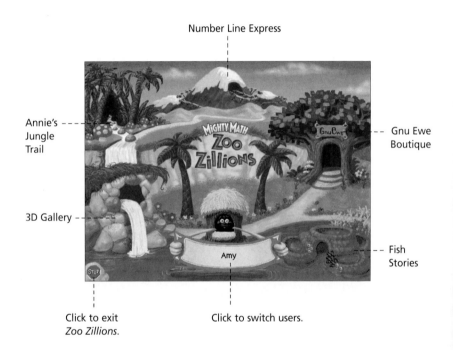 to return to the Zoo Entrance.

Number Line Express

Annie's Jungle Trail

Gnu Ewe Boutique

3D Gallery

Fish Stories

Click to exit *Zoo Zillions*.

Click to switch users.

Fish Stories

Move fish in and out of tanks to practice addition, subtraction, early multiplication, and early division. The results of your actions are reflected three ways: in pictures, in spoken and written sentences, and in a mathematical equation. With Fish Stories, it's easy to make the connection between concrete manipulatives, numbers, and words!

Gnu Ewe Boutique

Dress the zoo animals in outrageous outfits as you learn about money. To help the animals make their purchases, you'll need to identify coins and bills and their values; make the connection between cash and its numerical representation; and count, add, and subtract amounts of money.

3D Gallery

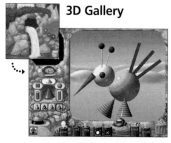

Sharpen your spatial skills and build math vocabulary as you learn to identify 3D solids—even when they turn in different directions or are partially hidden! Choose a 3D shape and watch it rotate. Freeze the shape at any angle, create a sticker of the shape, and use the shape sticker to make incredible 3D pictures and designs!

Annie's Jungle Trail

Review and practice basic math skills such as addition and subtraction, place value, skip counting, rounding, and mental math strategies in an exciting one-player or two-player game. As you solve problems, Annie and her friends invite you to spin the spinner and advance along the trail to meet up with some fun surprises.

Number Line Express

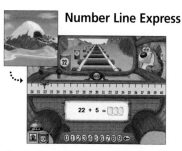

You're the engineer on the Number Line Express! Your animal friends need to get to stops located all over the zoo. To bring them to the right places, you'll locate numbers on the number line, add numbers to move forward on the number line, subtract numbers to move backward, and more.

Using Mighty Math Zoo Zillions

It's easy to explore all of the activities at the Mighty Math Zoo. To move from the Zoo Entrance to an activity, click one of these:

To return to the Zoo Entrance from an activity, click .

Question & Answer and Explore Modes

When you first enter an activity, you are in the Question & Answer Mode. Your Mighty Math friends take the lead, asking you questions and making requests. Fish Stories, the 3D Gallery, and the Number Line Express also have an Explore Mode. Ring the bell to enter the Explore Mode. Now you can experiment on your own. Play as long as you like. If you want to go back to the Question & Answer Mode, ring the bell again.

Grow Slides

As children successfully answer questions, the slider on the activity's Grow Slide automatically advances and more difficult questions are offered. (You can also adjust the Grow Slide manually.) There is a different Grow Slide for each activity.

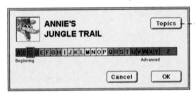

Click the Topics button to see a list of the topics covered as the slider advances. You can choose a specific topic for practice.

From an activity:
Children clics the *Grow Slide* button and then drag the slider to adjust the difficulty level or clicks the *Topics* button to select a math topic.

From Adult Options:
View the Grow Slides to monitor children's progress. You can also manually adjust the difficulty level of an activity to suit the child or choose to focus on a topic.
If you prefer, you can turn off children's access to the Grow Slides. (This will remove the *Grow Slide* buttons from the activities.)

Adult Options

To enter Adult Options, Windows users hold down the *Ctrl* and *Alt* keys while pressing "A." Macintosh users hold down the *Command*/⌘ and *Option* keys while pressing "A." Adult Options (see pages 24–25) allow you to customize *Zoo Zillions* to suit children.

Fish Stories Overview

Here are 2 yellow fish in a tank.
Put 3 red fish in the tank.
How many fish are now in the tank?

2 + 3 =

0 1 2 3 4 5 6 7 8 9

Join Eddie in the zoo's aquarium! In the Question & Answer Mode, children work with fish and tanks to solve story problems involving addition, subtraction, multiplication, and division. In the Explore Mode, children are free to explore the relationship between story problems, manipulatives, and equations.

Learning Opportunities

- Work with Virtual Manipulatives to illustrate and solve story problems
- Use counting, addition, subtraction, multiplication, and division to solve problems
- Discover and apply problem-solving strategies
- Review basic math facts

For many children, solving story problems (word problems) is the greatest challenge in elementary school mathematics. The early years of school are critical in developing children's skills and confidence in solving story problems. In kindergarten or earlier, children start to communicate their understanding of math through pictures, objects, and the use of spoken language; for example, "There are two cats in my picture." In the first and second grade, children increasingly use numbers and symbols to represent mathematical situations.

Fish Stories helps develop children's emerging ability to express a situation in mathematically meaningful ways. As children manipulate fish or numerals, the results are reflected on screen in pictures, spoken words, written words, numbers, and mathematical equations simultaneously. Children are challenged to create pictures to match the words, and to create mathematical equations to match the pictures. Encourage children to explain to you how they are using the picture of the fish to find the answer to a question posed in the story problem. Hearing their reasoning will tell you much about their mathematical thinking, and explaining the solution process to you deepens their understanding of the problem they are solving.

Question & Answer Mode

- From the Zoo Entrance, click [image] to play with Fish Stories.

- You are asked to solve a story problem by setting up the fish tanks, moving fish, and counting fish.

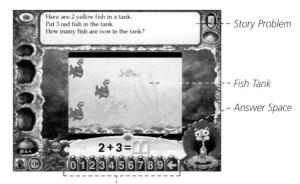

Here are 2 yellow fish in a tank.
Put 3 red fish in the tank.
How many fish are now in the tank?

Story Problem

Fish Tank

Answer Space

$2 + 3 = $

Number Bar

- Click the mouth [image] to hear the story problem repeated. (To hear a particular sentence repeated, click that sentence.)

- If you are asked to choose the number of tanks, click [image] to cycle through different numbers of tanks.

- Drag a fish from its cave to place it in a tank.

- If there are too many fish in the tank, drag a fish back to its cave.

- In subtraction problems, drag a fish to the right of the tank to make it "jump out."

- Click [image] to remove all the fish from the tanks or the numbers from the Answer Space.

- To enter a number of fish, click numbers on the Number Bar [image] . You can also type numbers from your computer's keyboard. To erase a number, click [image] .

- When you have completed the task or answered the question, click [image] .

  - If your answer is correct, you move on to the next part of the problem.

  - If your answer is not correct, Eddie helps you find the correct answer.

- Click the Grow Slide button [image] to change the difficulty level or content of the story problems.

- Ring the bell [image] to explore on your own, or click [image] to return to the Zoo Entrance.

Explore Mode

- Ring the bell 
Q&A
to enter the Explore Mode.
- You can experiment to see how moving the fish affects the story problem and the equation.

Hear your fish story read aloud.

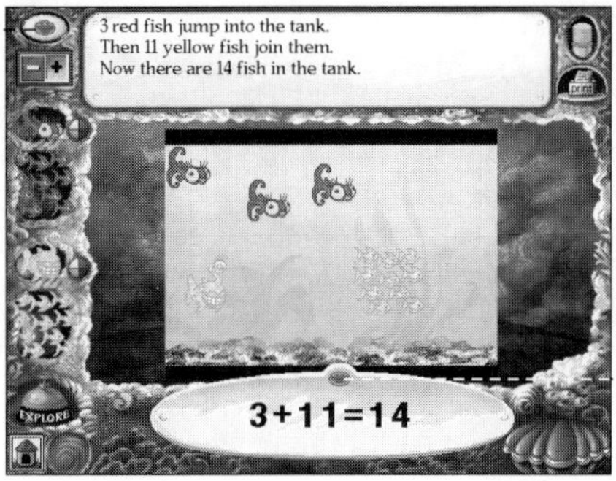
3 red fish jump into the tank.
Then 11 yellow fish join them.
Now there are 14 fish in the tank.
print
EXPLORE
3+11=14

Hear your equation read aloud.

- Click 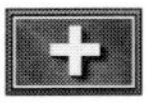 to make addition stories, or click 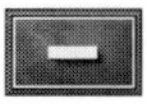 to make subtraction stories.
- Click  to change the color of the fish.
- Drag a fish  or a school of 10 fish 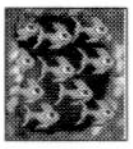 from the cave to place them in a tank.
- If there are too many fish in the tank, drag a fish back to its cave.
- In subtraction stories, drag a fish to the right of the tank to make it "jump out."
- To remove all the fish from the tank and start over, click .
- As you move fish, the fish story and equation change to match.
- Click a mouth  to hear your fish story or equation read aloud.
- To print your fish story, click 
print
.
- Ring the bell 
EXPLORE
to return to the Question & Answer Mode, or click  to return to the Zoo Entrance.

Gnu Ewe Boutique Overview

Allison needs your help in her chic Gnu Ewe Boutique, where the zoo animals come to spruce up their wardrobes. In the Question & Answer Mode, Allison provides training, starting with basic money concepts. As children learn and advance, they help customers with their purchases, total up purchases, and make change.

Learning Opportunities
- Recognize coins and bills and their values
- Count coins and bills
- Work with equivalencies
- Add and subtract money
- Use subtraction to give change
- Use cents (50¢) notation
- Explore decimals by using dollars and cents ($1.25) notation

Relating math to everyday life is important, because it makes mathematics meaningful and motivates children to learn about math. Money is one area in which mathematics relates directly to a child's life. However, while they may have an idea of the meaning and relevance of money, many young children do not have extensive experience using actual coins and bills. Given the opportunity to work with money in a meaningful way, children make important discoveries, such as learning that larger coins are not necessarily worth more and realizing that a given amount of money can be shown in several different ways by using different combinations of coins. As children work with money amounts in the Gnu Ewe Boutique, they will improve their ability to use money and will see the relevance of mathematics to everyday experiences. They can then apply their skill by being both a shopper and a clerk in the classroom store.

Question & Answer Mode

- From the Zoo Entrance, click to enter the Gnu Ewe Boutique.

- Allison and her customers ask you questions and make requests.

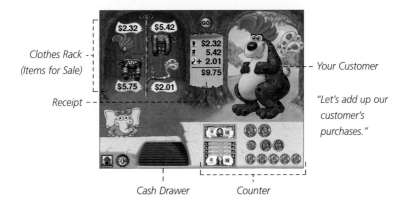

Clothes Rack
(Items for Sale)

Receipt

Your Customer

"Let's add up our
customer's
purchases."

Cash Drawer   Counter

- Click Allison or the customer to hear the question or request repeated.

- To give a customer change or to give Allison a requested coin or bill, click a coin or bill in the Cash Drawer. The selected money appears on the Counter, where the customer can take it.

- If there are too many coins or bills on the Counter, click a coin or bill on the Counter to put it back in the Cash Drawer.

- Click items on the Clothes Rack to select them for a customer. If you change your mind, click the item again to deselect it.

- When you are asked for a number, click numbers on the Number Bar **0123456789** to give your answer. You can also type numbers from your computer's keyboard. To change a number, click the number to select it, then click.

- When you have answered the question or completed the task, click **GO**.
  - If you have found the correct answer, you move on to the the next step of the problem.
  - If you have not found the correct answer, keep trying and you will find the right answer.

- Click the Grow Slide button to change the difficulty level of the problems or to choose a different math topic.

- Click to return to the Zoo Entrance.

3D Gallery Overview

Join the Otter Twins in their 3D Gallery. In the Question & Answer Mode, the twins display pictures in their gallery and ask children to find different 3D (three-dimensional) geometric shapes. In the Explore Mode, children can create their own pictures and designs with 3D images.

Learning Opportunities

- Develop spatial visualization skills
- Identify 3D geometric solids in various positions and orientations, including those in unusual views and those that are partially hidden
- Identify plane (two-dimensional) figures
- Relate real-world objects to corresponding geometric solids
- Build a vocabulary for describing geometric solids

A child's first experiences with geometry involve everyday 3D objects such as balls, cans; and boxes. Informal, hands-on exploration of these objects is important to a child's learning. As they explore geometric shapes, asking and answering questions about them, children learn first to recognize whole shapes and then to recognize the properties of shapes, such as the number of sides or the shape of the faces. Through many experiences that focus on geometric shapes and their direction, orientation, and perspective in space, children strengthen the spatial visualization skills that are essential for success in mathematics, in art, and in any type of problem-solving that uses visual models. As children work in the Question & Answer Mode of the 3D Gallery, they begin to build a geometry vocabulary by learning common and mathematical names of 3D shapes. When they work in the Explore Mode, children have many opportunities to investigate 3D shapes on their own and to experiment with the use of these 3D shapes, at many angles and in many positions, as they create their own designs.

Question & Answer Mode

- From the Zoo Entrance, click ▣ to play in the 3D Gallery.

- The Otter Twins ask you to find different 3D geometric shapes in the picture.

"Please find the box in the picture."

- Click one of the otters to hear the problem repeated.

- A variety of 3D geometric shapes appears in the picture.

- Click a shape ▲ in the picture to select it. Click the shape again to deselect it.

- Some questions are accompanied by a movie of a 3D shape.

- Click (FREEZE) to stop the movie.

- Click (PLAY) to play the movie.

- Click ☜ or ☞ to step backward or forward through the movie, one frame at a time.

- When you have solved the problem, click .

  - If your answer is correct, you are rewarded.

  - If your answer is not correct, the Otter Twins help you find the right answer.

- Click the Grow Slide button ▣ to change the difficulty level of the Otter Twins' problems or to select a different math topic.

- Ring the bell 🔔 to enter the Explore Mode, or click ▣ to return to the Zoo Entrance.

Explore Mode

- Ring the bell to enter the Explore Mode.

- Create your own pictures with different backgrounds and 3D shapes.

Movie Screen - - -

Shapes - -

Movie Grid - -

Workspace

- Click to see some fun picture ideas.

Choose a Shape

- Click a shape button to choose that shape.

- Variations of the shape appear in the Movie Grid.

- Click or to see more variations.

Play with the Movie

- Click a shape variation on the Movie Grid and it appears on the Movie Screen.

- Click to play the movie.

- Click to freeze the movie in place.

- Click or to step backward or forward through the movie, one frame at a time.

- When the movie is frozen, the shape can be used as a sticker. Drag the shape from the Movie Screen to the Workspace.

Make a Picture

- Drag a sticker around the Workspace to move it.

- Click a sticker to select it, then click 🔘 to make it larger, or click 🔳 to make it smaller.

- To remove an individual shape from the Workspace, drag it to the Trash Can 🗑.

- To erase all the shapes from the Workspace , click 🔳.

- Click 🔵 to switch to another background.

Printing, Saving, and Opening Pictures

- Click 🖨 to print your picture.

- Click 💾 to save your picture. Drag the miniaturized version (thumbnail) of the picture to an empty rectangle. Click ☐ OK ☐ to save the picture. To delete a previously saved picture, drag the thumbnail of the unwanted picture to the trash can. Click ☐ OK ☐ to empty the trash can.

- Click 📂 to open a previously saved picture. Click the thumbnail of the picture you want to open. Click ☐ OK ☐ to view or change the picture.

- Hold down the Ctrl key (Windows) or Option key (Macintosh) while clicking 💾 or 📂 to save or open 3D Gallery files on your hard drive, using a standard Windows or Macintosh "Save" dialog. These files can then be transferred to other computers and traded with your friends.

- Ring the bell 🔔 to return to the Question & Answer Mode, or click 🏠 to return to the Zoo Entrance.

Annie's Jungle Trail Overview

Whether it's a hoot 'n' holler from Annie or a wild ride down the waterfall, there are lots of surprises along Annie's Jungle Trail! Children enjoy practicing math skills such as addition, subtraction, skip counting, and rounding numbers to the nearest 10 as they race through the jungle. Children can challenge themselves or another student in this one- or two-player game.

Learning Opportunities
- Use addition and subtraction facts
- Identify the missing number in an addition or subtraction sentence
- Use mental math strategies to solve addition and subtraction problems
- Skip count by twos, fives, and tens
- Round numbers to the nearest ten
- Identify the missing number in a pattern
- Compare addition and subtraction expressions

When children understand the concepts behind basic math facts, the facts are more meaningful to them and their retention of the facts is stronger. Many activities in *Zoo Zillions*, such as Fish Stories and Number Line Express, build this understanding of math concepts through the use of Virtual Manipulatives. While understanding math concepts is crucial, practice with basic math facts is also important. If children do not know basic subtraction facts, they will not be able to do long division—or algebra. The focus in Annie's Jungle Trail is on practice with math facts, so that children can gain fluency with them. Young children are intrigued by games and like to play the same game over and over. The fun of playing with Annie's Jungle Trail game motivates children to spend hours solving addition, subtraction, place value, and many other problems, building their knowledge of basic math facts and gaining valuable experience in "mental math"—the ability to solve problems without paper, pencil, or calculator.

Question & Answer Mode

- From the Zoo Entrance, click [img] to play on Annie's Jungle Trail.

- Annie asks you to choose the number of players and to pick a game piece.

- Click (1 Player) for a one-player game, or click (2 Players) for a two-player game.

- Choose a game piece [img] by dragging it into the Game Piece Space [img] .

- Advance to the end of the trail by finding the answers to math problems.

Spinner

"Find the total."

Answer Space

Number Bar

- In a two-player game, (in the lower right corner of the screen) shows your piece if it is your turn; it shows your friend's piece if it is your friend's turn.

- Annie asks you to click the spinner [img] .

- A math problem is read aloud.

- Click the mouth [img] to hear the problem again.

- Click numbers on the Number Bar (0123456789⊝) to give your answer. You can also type numbers from your computer's keyboard. To erase a number, click [img].

- Some questions must be answered with "yes" or "no," "even" or "odd." Two words pop up in place of the Number Bar. Click a word to select your answer.

- When you think you have the answer, click .

  - If your answer is correct, your game piece moves the number of spaces indicated by the spinner.

  - If your answer is not correct, the number selected on the Spinner decreases by one. Annie helps you find the right answer.

- Click **NEW** to start a new game.

- Click the Grow Slide button ⊞ to change the difficulty level of the questions or to choose a different math topic.

- Click 🏠 to return to the Zoo Entrance.

Number Line Express Overview

All aboard! Explore the zoo on the Number Line Express! Children use a number line to help them locate, pick up, and drop off passengers all over the zoo. Ryan Lion is waiting at the dispatch center, ready to tell children where to find their next pick-up. Young engineers take control of the train as they navigate the number line by locating numbers, counting backward and forward, adding, subtracting, and finding missing addends.

Learning Opportunities:
- Locate a number on a number line
- Count backward and forward using the number line
- Use the number line to add and subtract
- Use a number line to identify the missing number in an addition or subtraction sentence
- Build equations and recognize their relationship to the number line

Very young children learn best when they can see, feel, and touch. They need experiences using concrete, hands-on manipulatives to build number sense, to count, and to model addition and subtraction problems. Through the use of these manipulatives, children build powerful concepts about numbers. As children's thinking advances, they are able to use more abstract models, such as maps, to help them understand the world. The number line is a powerful "map" that children can use to understand numbers and number relationships. As children scan the number line in Number Line Express, they can "see" the distance between two numbers. They discover that moving forward from 0 always brings them to larger numbers. The number line also gives children another way to think about addition; addition can be thought of as "counting forward" from a number. (To add 5 to 10, kids can start at 10 and move forward 5 stops.) Children can also use the number line to help them master counting backward and to understand subtraction as "counting backward" from a number.

Question & Answer Mode

- From the Zoo Entrance, click [image] to play with the Number Line Express.

- Ryan asks you to pick up a passenger, or a passenger asks to be dropped off.

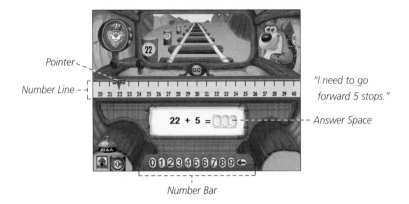

- Click Ryan or the passenger to hear the request repeated.

- You can move along the number line in one of two ways: by dragging the Pointer on the number line or by clicking numbers on the Number Bar.

- If the Number Line Pointer [image] is available, you can drag the Pointer to the place you want to go.

- If the Number Bar [image] is available, you can click numbers on the Number Bar to show the answer. You can also type numbers from your computer's keyboard. To erase a number, click [image].

- When you think you have the right answer, click [image].

  - If your answer is correct, the train moves to the location you indicated.

  - If your answer is not correct, Ryan helps you find the right answer.

- Click the Grow Slide button [image] to change the difficulty level of the problems or to choose another math topic.

- Ring the bell [image] to enter the Explore Mode, or click [image] to return to the Zoo Entrance.

Explore Mode

- Ring the bell 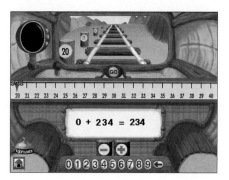 to enter the Explore Mode.

- Move the train along the number line by creating addition and subtraction equations.

- Click ![plus] to create an addition problem, or click ![minus] to create a subtraction problem.

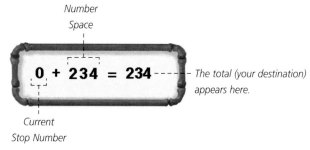

Number Space

$$\underbrace{0}_{\substack{\text{Current}\\ \text{Stop Number}}} + \underbrace{234}_{} = 234 \quad \text{---} \quad \textit{The total (your destination) appears here.}$$

- Click numbers on the Number Bar ![number bar] to enter them in the Number Space. (To erase a number, click ![erase].) Starting at the current stop, the program adds or subtracts your entry to calculate the total.

- Click ![GO] to travel to the total shown.

- Ring the bell ![bell] to return to the Question & Answer Mode, or click ![home] to return to the Zoo Entrance.

Adult Options

To enter Adult Options, Windows users hold down the *Ctrl* and *Alt* keys while pressing "A." Macintosh users hold down the *Command⌘* and *Option* keys while pressing "A."

Use Adult Options to change preference settings for *Zoo Zillions*, control the Grow Slide settings, and modify the User List.

Preferences

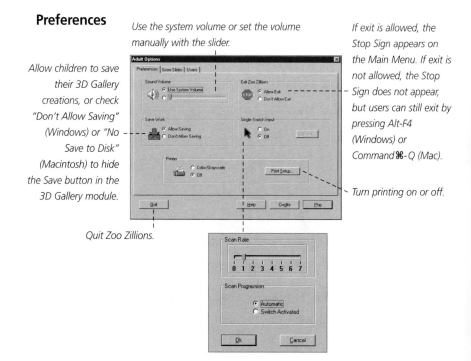

Use the system volume or set the volume manually with the slider.

If exit is allowed, the Stop Sign appears on the Main Menu. If exit is not allowed, the Stop Sign does not appear, but users can still exit by pressing Alt-F4 (Windows) or Command⌘-Q (Mac).

Allow children to save their 3D Gallery creations, or check "Don't Allow Saving" (Windows) or "No Save to Disk" (Macintosh) to hide the Save button in the 3D Gallery module.

Turn printing on or off.

Quit Zoo Zillions.

Single Switch Input Options for Children with Special Needs

Built-in scanning is available for single switch users in Fish Stories, the Gnu Ewe Boutique, and Annie's Jungle Trail. Turn "Single Switch Input" on and click `Options...` .

■ Choose the type of Scan Progression.

Automatic Progression: Scanning restarts automatically after each selection.

Switch Activated Progression: Switch required to restart scanning after each selection.

■ Select the scanning rate (in seconds): 1 (fastest) to 7 (slowest).

When scanning is on, you can temporarily suspend or resume scanning by pressing Ctrl-Alt-S (Windows) or Command⌘-Option-S (Macintosh).

Grow Slides/Activity Settings

Adjustable Grow Slides allow you to monitor children's progress or set an activity to focus on a particular math topic. As children successfully solve problems, the slider automatically advances to more difficult problems. Click the "Grow Slides" (Windows) or "Activity Settings" (Macintosh) tab in Adult Options to adjust the Grow Slide settings and options.

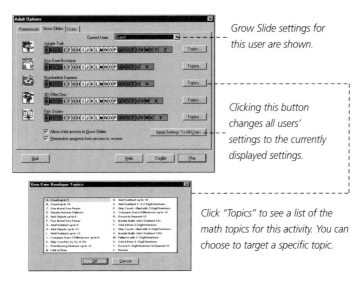

Grow Slide settings for this user are shown.

Clicking this button changes all users' settings to the currently displayed settings.

Click "Topics" to see a list of the math topics for this activity. You can choose to target a specific topic.

- Check "Remember progress from session to session" if you want *Zoo Zillions* to save children's progress in each activity when they exit the program. If "Remember progress…" is unchecked, *Zoo Zillions* will always begin at the settings that are currently displayed on the Grow Slides. (To change the settings, you will need to open the Grow Slides and change them manually.)

- Check "Allow child access to Grow Slides" if you want children to be able to adjust the topic or the level of difficulty. If "Allow child access to Grow Slides" is unchecked, the Grow Slide buttons do not appear within the activities.

Users

- To remove a name from the User List, select the name and click [Remove]. (You cannot remove the current user or the "Guest" user.)
- To rename a user, select the name and click [Rename].
- To add a name to the User List, click [Add] and type the name.

If the "Allow New Users to Add Themselves" box is checked, children can add their names to the User List at the Zoo Entrance. Uncheck this box if you do not want children to add their own names.

KidDesk Aware

If *Zoo Zillions* is launched from *KidDesk*, the *KidDesk* user is signed in automatically and the User List does not appear. To switch users, return to *KidDesk* and open a different desk.

Scanning settings are taken from *KidDesk*.

The Stop Sign at the Zoo Entrance is replaced by the *KidDesk* icon. Clicking the icon returns the user to *KidDesk*.

Options for Classroom Use

Zoo Zillions can be introduced to children in a variety of ways. As you explore the program, consider their learning styles and what might be most helpful in getting them started. Use the Adult Options to set *Zoo Zillions* to best suit children's needs. (See page 24.)

Fish Stories: Salad Stories Help a small group of children tell a story problem that becomes a recipe for fruit salad. Gather a variety of fruits together and cut them into pieces. Ask children which fruits they want to put into the salad. Have them draw a small picture of each kind of fruit on an index card. Put a few pieces of one type of fruit in a small bowl as you narrate your actions.

Example:

> First, I added 4 banana slices to the salad. (Have a volunteer add a few pieces of the same fruit, while you narrate the child's actions.)

> Then, you added 6 banana slices. How many slices are in the salad?

Help children find the answer, and then ask one child to write the number 10 next to the picture of the banana on the card. Repeat the activity with each type of fruit.

Children may then use Fish Stories to solve story problems.

Gnu Ewe Boutique: Everyday Money Have a small group of children pretend they are shopping in a grocery store. Label different-sized boxes with various prices. Each child can spend $3.00 to buy a box of cereal. Discuss which cereals could be bought, and which couldn't. If each child had $6.00 to spend for two boxes of cereal, which ones could they buy? Children may enjoy using a calculator to add up their total purchases.

Children may then use Gnu Ewe Boutique to learn to count money, make change, and add and subtract decimals.

3D Gallery: 3D Mysteries Play some guessing games with children to develop their understanding of 3D shapes. Gather a variety of objects in basic 3D shapes. (For example, use a tin can for a cylinder, a box for a cube, and an ice-cream cone for a cone; or use building blocks.) Show children the objects, and help them identify each shape. Then place one object in a bag. (Be sure children can't tell which object it is.) Ask volunteers to place a hand in the bag to feel the object and guess what shape it is.

Another guessing game is a variation of the classic 20 Questions. Place all of the 3D shapes you have collected on a table and ask a child to choose one, without telling you which it is. Then ask yes or no questions about the shape until you can guess what it is. "Does it roll?" "Does it have any rounded edges?" Reverse roles. You choose a shape, and the child guesses. Pairs of children can play once they know the rules.

Children may then use 3D Gallery to explore movies of 3D solids and create 3D designs.

Annie's Jungle Trail: How Many in That Crowd? Write the number 10 on a large piece of paper, and 20 on another. Do the same for the numbers 30, 40, and 50. Spread these number sheets on a table. Have children look through old magazines to find pictures that show many of one thing, for example a crowd of people, a garden of flowers, a row of houses. Have them cut out each picture, count the objects in it, and write the number on the picture. Then help children round the number to the nearest 10 and place the number on the appropriate number sheet. Example:

> A child may label one picture 12 people. Ask whether 12 is closer to 10 or 20.
>
> Help him or her find the answer and place the picture on the sheet marked 10.

When children are finished, you can have them paste the pictures onto the number sheets, or you can keep the pictures to sort again at another time.

Children may then use Annie's Jungle Trail to practice addition, subtraction, and skip counting.

Number Line Express: Personal-History Number Line

Pairs of children can make personally meaningful number lines. Use sheets of construction paper in different colors. On the first page, write a large number 0, on the second write 1, and so on either up to the children's ages or up to 10. Help children write both a word sentence and a number sentence for each page. Example:

> On the page for the number 5, a 6-year-old might write, "1 year ago I was 5. 6 − 1 = 5." The child might then draw a picture of how he or she looked at that age.

> On the page for the number 8, a 6-year-old might write, "In 2 years I will be 8. 6 + 2 = 8." The child might draw a picture of something he or she would like to do at that age.

Encourage children to be creative and to use their own ideas for each page. Tape the finished pages together in order, from 0 to 10. Hang the completed number line for display.

Children may then use Number Line Express to count forward and backward and to add and subtract on a number line.

Grow Slide Levels

Each of the five learning activities in *Zoo Zillions* has a Grow Slide with levels of difficulty that increase from A up to Z.

Gnu Ewe Boutique
A. Value of a Penny, Nickel, and Dime
B. Penny, Nickel, and Dime Equivalents
C. Count Pennies to 9¢
D. Value of a Quarter
E. Count Coins to 50¢
F. Count Coins to 75¢
G. Nickel, Dime, and Quarter Equivalents
H. Count Coins to 99¢
I. Add 2 Amounts to 15¢
J. Subtract to Make Change (Basic Facts)
K. Value of a $1 Bill
L. Dime and Dollar Equivalents
M. Quarter and Dollar Equivalents
N. Value of a $5 and a $10 Bill
O. Coin and Bill Equivalents to $10
P. Add Dollar Amount to $9
Q. Subtract to Make Change (Dollars)
R. Count Bills and Coins to $10
S. Add 2 or 3 Amounts to 99¢
T. Add Dollar Amounts to $99
U. Add 2 or 3 Amounts to $9.99
V. Review

Fish Stories
A. Addition Stories – to 6
B. Subtraction Stories – from 6
C. Addition Stories – to 12
D. Subtraction Stories – from 12
E. Comparison Stories – to 9
F. Missing Number Stories – to 9
G. Stories with 2 Equal Groups
H. Divide up to 12
I. Addition Stories-to 18
J. Subtraction Stories – from 18
K. Addition Stories – to 29
L. Subtraction Stories – from 29
M. Comparison Stories – to 18
N. Subtraction Stories with Comparing
O. Missing Number in Subtraction
P. 2-Digit Addition Stories
Q. 2-Digit Subtraction Stories
R. Addition – Missing First Number
S. Subtraction – Missing First Number
T. 2-Digit Comparison Stories
U. Addition Stories with Comparing
V. Multiplication Stories – to 24
W. Division Stories – Sharing
X. Division Stories – Separating
Y. Review

3D Gallery
A. Match Box to Example
B. Match Ball to Example
C. Match Can to Example
D. Match Cone to Example
E. Identify a Box
F. Identify a Ball
G. Identify a Can
H. Identify a Cone
I. Match Cube, Sphere, Cylinder, Cone
J. Identify Cube, Sphere, Cylinder, Cone
K. Identify Partially Hidden Solids
L. Match Rectangular Prism to Example
M. Identify Rectangular Prism
N. Solids and Their Faces
O. Unusual Views of Cubes
P. Unusual Views of Cylinders
Q. Unusual Views of Rectangular Prisms
R. Unusual Views of Cones
S. Unusual Views of Hidden Cubes
T. Unusual Views of Hidden Spheres
U. Unusual Views of Hidden Cylinders
V. Unusual Views of Hidden Rect. Prisms
W. Unusual Views of Hidden Cones
X. Review

Annie's Jungle Trail
A. Count up to 10
B. Add Object up to 6
C. Add/Subtract up to 6
D. Add Objects up to 10
E. Add/Subtract up to 12
F. Compare Sums/Differences up to 6
G. Skip Count by 2s, 5s, & 10s
H. Find Missing Number up to 12
I. Odd or Even
J. Compare Sums/Differences up to 12
K. Add/Subtract up to 18
L. Add/Subtract 1- & 2-Digit Numbers
M. Skip Count – Start with 2-Digit Numbers
N. Patterns with 2-Digit Numbers
O. Compare Sums/Differences up to 18
P. Round to Nearest 10
Q. Mental Math: Add/Subtract 10s
R. Odd & Even 2-Digit Numbers
S. Skip Count – Start with 3-Digit Numbers
T. Mental Math: Add/Subtract 100s
U. Patterns with 3-Digit Numbers
V. Odd & Even 3-Digit Numbers
W. Round 3-Digit Numbers to Nearest 10
X. Review

Number Line Express
A. 0 to 10: Locate Numbers
B. 0 to 10 : Move Forward/Back
C. 0 to 10: Add/Subtract up to 6
D. 0 to 20: Move Forward/Back
E. 0 to 20: Add/Subtract – Basic Facts
F. 0 to 20: Find Missing Number
G. 20 to 40: Move Forward/Back
H. 20 to 40: Add/Subtract
I. 20 to 40: Find Missing Numbers
J. 40 to 100: Move Forward/Back
K. 40 to 100: Add/Subtract
L. 40 to 100: Find Missing Numbers
M. 90 to 110: Move Forward/Back
N. 90 to 110: Add/Subtract
O. 90 to 110: Find Missing Numbers
P. 100 to 300: Move Forward/Back
Q. 100 to 300: Add/Subtract
R. 100 to 300: Find Missing Numbers
S. 300 to 990: Move Forward/Back
T. 300 to 990: Add/Subtract
U. 300 to 990: Find Missing Numbers
V. Review

Troubleshooting—Windows

Problem	Possible Cause	Solution
Missing one or more necessary system components.	Not enough hard disk space to install *Zoo Zillions*.	Free up an additional 5 MB of hard disk space.
Program interrupted by any error message.	Dirty CD.	Clean CD. (Use soft cotton cloth or CD cleaner.)
No sound.	Volume set too low.	Use your sound card's control panel to increase the computer's volume, or use the volume control in Adult Options (page 24).
	Speaker is turned off.	Turn speaker on.
	"Mute" enabled in Win95.	Turn off "Mute" in Win95. (See your *Win95 User's Guide*.)
	Sound device not installed properly for Windows.	Consult your sound device manual.
Unable to print.	Printing has been turned off in Adult Options.	Turn printing on in Adult Options (page 24).
	Out of paper/printer turned off.	Check printer.
	No default printer selected.	Select your printer in the Windows control panel.
	Incorrect printer settings.	Check printer control panel in Windows.
On-screen colors are wrong or garbled.	Incompatible video driver.	Try a 640x480, 256-color setting, or contact your video card manufacturer for information on obtaining the latest video driver.
Mouse cursor hidden and large arrow appears on screen.	Single switch input (scanning) is on in Adult Options.	Click Single Switch Input (scanning) "Off" in Adult Options (page 24).
Screen flashes and returns to Program Manager when running from Windows 3.1x.	Win32s not installed properly.	Run setup from the CD again. (See Setup Instructions, page 3).
Unexplained errors.	Video driver conflict.	Update video driver.
	Conflict with another program.	Remove programs from the Startup group. Remove programs from the Load= and Run= lines of WIN.INI

Troubleshooting—Macintosh

Problem	Possible Cause	Solution
Zoo Zillions icon does not appear on desktop.	External CD-ROM drive is not turned on.	Make sure your CD-ROM drive is turned on before you start your computer (external drives only).
	The correct CD-ROM drive extension is not present.	Check the Extensions folder (in your System Folder) to ensure that it contains the correct CD-ROM extension for your CD-ROM drive.
Program interrupted by any error message.	Dirty CD.	Clean CD. (Use soft cotton cloth or CD cleaner.)
Sound breaks up.	Virtual Memory is on.	Turn Virtual Memory off from the Memory control panel. (See your *Macintosh User's Guide*.)
Sound is too quiet or too loud.	Sound volume needs to be adjusted.	Adjust the volume for *Zoo Zillions* using the Sound Volume control in Adult Options (page 24).
Mouse cursor hidden and large arrow appears on screen.	Single switch input (scanning) is on.	Click Single Switch Input (scanning) "off" in Adult Options (page 24).
Picture or text does not print.	Out of paper/printer turned off.	Check printer.
	Printer cables are incorrectly attached.	Check cable attachments. Refer to printer manual.
	Incorrect printer is selected in "Chooser."	Use the "Chooser" (from Apple menu) to set the desired printer and options.
Printing icon does not appear in activities.	Printing is turned off.	Turn printing on in Adult Options (page 24).
Open and Save icons do not appear in 3D Gallery.	Saving is turned off.	Click "Allow Save to Disk" in "Adult Options" (page 24).
Your monitor does not display color on a color monitor.	Monitor is set to display "Grays."	Use Monitors Control Panel to set to "Colors" instead of "Grays." (See the *Macintosh User's Guide*.)
3D Gallery will not run.	Conflict with file sharing.	Turn file sharing off from the Sharing Setup control panel.
Movies do not play in 3D Gallery.	QuickTime is missing.	Open the QuickTime™ Files folder (included on the *Zoo Zillions* CD); drag the QuickTime and QuickTime Power Plug icons into your System Folder.

Technical Help

If you experience difficulties installing or running this software, please consult the Troubleshooting pages in this Guide. If you do not find a solution, please contact **Harcourt Brace Technical Support** using one of the numbers below.

Technology Service Hotline
1-800-419-3900

Fax on Demand Service
1-800-352-1680

Interactive Technical Support on the Web
http://www.hbtechsupport.com.

Software License Agreement and Limited Warranty

License This program is licensed for use on one computer. It is against U.S. copyright law to copy this program for use by others, to install the program on more than one hard drive, or to network the program for use on more than one computer. Requests for permission to make copies of any part of the program should be mailed to: Permissions Department, Harcourt Brace & Company, 6277 Sea Harbor Drive, Orlando Florida 32887-6777.

Teachers may make additional copies of the activity and artwork pages of the *Teacher's Guide* to use with students.

Additional Discs When you order a basic CD-ROM package you may order additional CD-ROM discs at reduced prices. To order call **Customer Service** at **1-800-225-5425.**

Warranty and Replacements Harcourt Brace School Publishers warrants the software against defects or damage for 60 days from the invoice date.

Technology Service Hotline If you have a technical question about installing or running the software, please call **1-800-419-3900** for assistance.

Software Copyright Notice

The Learning Site

at http://www.hbschool.com

A World Wide Web service from Harcourt Brace, with resources for students, teachers, and parents

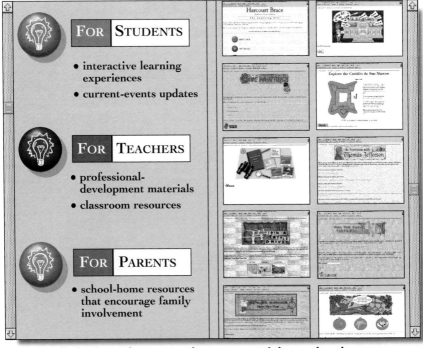

FOR STUDENTS
- interactive learning experiences
- current-events updates

FOR TEACHERS
- professional-development materials
- classroom resources

FOR PARENTS
- school-home resources that encourage family involvement

All designed to complement, enrich, and enhance Harcourt Brace publications.

The Mighty Math Series

Grades K-3	Grades 3-6	Grades 6-8
Carnival Countdown	**Number Heroes**	**Cosmic Geometry**
✔ Problem Solving & Logic	✔ Problem Solving, Patterns, & Logic	**Builds a Foundation for Geometry**
✔ Place Value (1's, 10's, and 100's)	✔ Addition & Subtraction	✔ Attributes of Shapes & Solids
✔ Addition & Subtraction	✔ Multiplication & Division	✔ Constructions & Transformations
✔ Sorting & Classification	✔ Fractions (Add, Subtract, & Multiply)	✔ 2D & 3D Coordinates
✔ Early Multiplication & Division	✔ Geometry (Angles, Perimeter, Area)	✔ Length, Perimeter, & Area
✔ Equivalencies (<, >, and =)	✔ Probability, Graphs, & Charts	✔ Surface Area & Volume
Zoo Zillions	**Calculating Crew**	**Astro Algebra**
✔ Problem Solving & Reasoning	✔ Problem Solving & Reasoning	**Builds a Foundation for Algebra**
✔ Number Line Concepts & Counting	✔ Money Transactions	✔ Variables
✔ Counting Money & Making Change	✔ Estimation & Rounding	✔ Expressions, Equations, & Inequalities
✔ Addition & Subtraction Facts	✔ 1- to 4-Digit Addition & Subtraction	✔ Functions & Graphing
✔ Story Problems (with +, −, x, and ÷)	✔ 1- to 3-Digit Multiplication & Division	✔ Ratios & Proportions
✔ Early 3D Geometry	✔ 3D Geometry (Solids & Nets)	✔ Fractions, Decimals, & Percents

Integrating Technology

Mathematics skills are essential life skills. Everyone must be proficient in basic mathematical skills to function in our world. Today's children will live and work in the world of the twenty-first century that will continue to change in response to the growth of scientific and technological knowledge. Since computers are a basic tool in today's society, they have changed the way children learn mathematics and the way teachers teach mathematics. In math instruction and practice, children often use computers to investigate fundamental mathematical topics and to formulate and solve problems.

Meeting Individual Needs Through Integrated Technology Components

With the Grow Slides available in *Zoo Zillions*, you are able to target specific needs of children. Grow Slides list the wide breadth of math problems and topics in each activity. As children succeed, Grow Slides automatically advance, offering more challenging topics and problems. Use Grow Slides to:

- adjust the difficulty level.

- choose a specific topic.

- monitor progress.

(See page 28 for Grow Slide levels.)

Integrated technology connections in math programs are designed to invite exploration and challenge children to see the power and value of mathematics. The auditory and visual prompts in *Zoo Zillions* encourage success, act as models for children, and help them to remain on task. Since computers have infinite patience, all children can learn new concepts at their own pace.

Computers using such programs as *Zoo Zillions* have even greater potential to assist in further restructuring school mathematics by motivating children and by helping them form connections between mathematics and their everyday experiences — all ways to enhance learning and put excitement into the teaching of mathematics!

What's Inside Zoo Zillions

Number Line Express

Annie's
Jungle
Trail

Gnu Ewe
Boutique

3D Gallery

Fish
Stories

HARCOUR
BRAC
ISBN 0-15-30797